AVRO CF-105 ARROW
CANADA'S SUPERSONIC SENTINEL

MARC-ANDRÉ VALIQUETTE
IMAVIATION

AVRO CF-105 ARROW
CANADA'S SUPERSONIC SENTINEL

Copyright © Marc-André Valiquette 2014

ISBN 978-2-9811552-6-9

ISBN 978-2-9811552-7-6
(Version française / Avro CF-105 Arrow, La sentinelle supersonique canadienne)

Legal Deposit - Library and Archives Canada, 2014

Dépôt légal - Bibliothèque et Archives nationales du Québec, 2014

Valiquette, Marc-André, 1958 -

Avro CF-105 Arrow - Canada's Supersonic sentinel

    - ISBN 978-2-9811552-6-9
    - 1. Arrow....Aviation
    - 2. Canadian Military.....Aviation
    - 3. Photo collection

Design: Jean-François Mongeau
Publisher: IMAVIATION

Printed and bound in Canada by Friesens Corporation, Altona, Manitoba, Canada

This book has entirely been designed and produced in Canada, without any government financial support .

Contact us:
IMAVIATION / Marc-André Valiquette
arrow201@videotron.ca
www.avrocanada-arrow.ca

Cover page painting by David Reppen / Avro Canada 1958

This book is not the result of just one person but of many. A special thank you must go to Robert Cohen, Louise Gince, Richard Girouard, Frank Harvey, Bruce McLeod, Keith Meredith, Stephen Quick, Anne Renwick, Robert St-Pierre, Hélène Trudel, Bill Upton and Bruno Zaroal.

Photograph credits: Canada Aviation and Space Museum (owner of the Avro / Hawker Siddeley negatives collection), Canadian Forces Joint Imagery Centre (CFJIC), National Defence Image Library, AHFC and the Canadian Air and Space Museum.

Avro and Orenda document credits: Collection Marc-André Valiquette and Air Defence Museum, 3 Wing Bagotville, QC.

CONTENTS

FOREWORD

The Arrow represented a dream and an unprecedented business opportunity for Avro Canada, a critical operational requirement for the RCAF, and a next generation interceptor which became prohibitively expensive and strategically unnecessary for the Diefenbaker government.

Canada's Supersonic Sentinel is a "must-read" for aviation enthusiasts and historians alike. Marc-André Valiquette takes the reader on an eloquent and illustrative journey to show that the Arrow's cancellation was a watershed moment for the Canadian aviation industry.

It resulted in the infamous "brain drain" of remarkable intellect and engineering acumen to other aerospace companies in the US and the UK, including NASA. It also resulted in the loss of, what could have been incredible economic and industrial benefits for Canada.

Even if one postulates the decision to destroy all Arrow prototypes was unavoidable from a national security perspective, the loss of these extraordinary artefacts was, nonetheless, a tragic squandering of Canadian history and ingenuity.

As the Commanding Officer of Canada's eastern CF-18 squadron and an experienced "Hornet" driver myself, I can assure you that it is our sense of loyalty and duty which prescribes fighter pilots to courageously fly whatever aircraft our government provides. However, the CF-105 Arrow was an example that the primacy of strategic requirements and operational performance are often superseded by economics and politics.

As you read this story and potentially engage in future fighter procurement debates, it is important to remember there are men and women at the pointy end of the military-industrial complex where performance does make the difference between life and death.

Lieutenant-Colonel Darcy E. Molstad
Commanding Officer, 425 Tactical Fighter Squadron
Royal Canadian Air Force

Avro employees at Arrow rollout
October 4, 1957

DEDICATION

In honour of the men and women of the Canadian aerospace industry who in the 1950's, put their dynamism, creativeness and faith into the country's foremost national defence project.

The Arrow interceptor was meant to protect Canadians from a Cold War enemy, yet was destroyed by its own leaders.

"A generation which ignores history has no past - and no future."

Robert A. Heinlein,
American science fiction writer

Avro NEWSMAGAZINE

Name J.L. Plant Avro President

Company Pilots Testing Missiles At USN Base

VOL. 4, NO. 5   PUBLISHED TWICE MONTHLY BY AVRO AIRCRAFT LIMITED   APRIL 24, 1958

With afterburners spewing fire, the Arrow 1 is shown in a climb during a recent test flight at Malton.

Arrow Exceeds 1,000 MPH On Seventh Flight

Avro NEWSMAGAZINE

THE ARROW STORY

SPECIAL EDITION   PUBLISHED BY AVRO AIRCRAFT LIMITED   SUMMER, 1958

FROM CONCEPT TO FLIGHT TEST

SUPERSONIC SENTINEL

RCAF SPECIFICATION AIR 7-3

Avro Canada and Orenda Engines Plants, 1957

In 1952, the increased threat on Europe from the Soviet Union convinces the RCAF to start looking for an all-weather supersonic interceptor. Specifics of the Air Force requirements and the non-availability of a suitable weapon system elsewhere lead to the conclusion that the new aircraft has to be designed, developed and manufactured by Avro Canada of Malton, Ontario.

CF-105 Design Team

In May of 1953, the RCAF issues Specification AIR 7-3 (later AIR 7-4) which becomes the basis of Avro's design studies. The CF-105 design team is composed of Robert L. Lindley, Chief Engineer; Jim C. Floyd, Vice-President Engineering; Guest Hake, Project Designer; and Jim Chamberlin, Chief Aerodynamicist.

Early CF-105 Model

CF-105 Arrow Mk.1 structure cutaway
Drawing: Brett Reid

A high thin wing delta tailless design is chosen because of its structural and aero-elastic efficiency. This configuration accommodates the internal fuel capacity, provides excellent access to the engines and allows for the required weapons bay dimensions. The aircraft is to be equipped with two turbojet engines and an integrated Fire Control System. The armament will consist of air-to-air missiles and air-to-air-rockets.

The basic requirement is for a two man, twin engine aircraft with a combat radius of action at supersonic speed of 230 miles (370 km) and a ferry range of 1,725 miles (2,775 km). The most stringent requirement is manoeuvrability which is defined as a combat load factor of 2g at a combat speed of Mach 1.5 (990 mph - 1,593 km/h), and at a combat altitude of 50,000 feet (15,240 m) without the loss of speed and altitude.

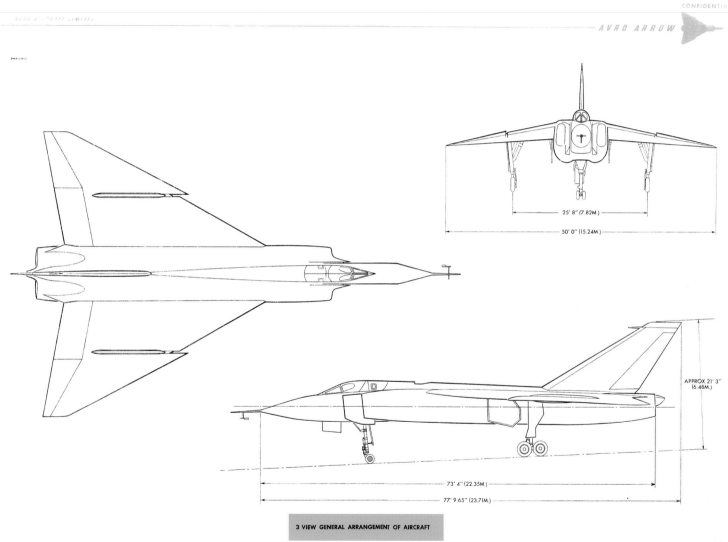

CONFIDENTIAL

AVRO ARROW

25' 8" (7.82M.)

50' 0" (15.24M.)

APPROX 21' 3"
(6.48M.)

73' 4" (22.35M.)

77' 9.65" (23.71M.)

3 VIEW GENERAL ARRANGEMENT OF AIRCRAFT

14

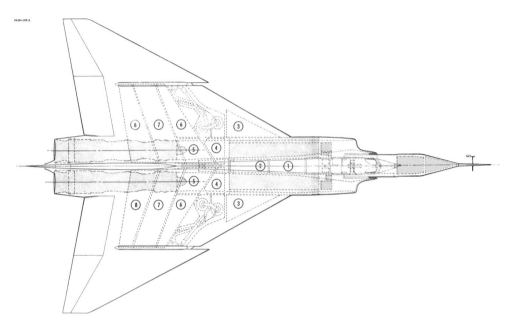

TANK	LOCATION	CAPACITY	
		IMP. GAL.	LB.
1	FUSELAGE	252	1890
2	FUSELAGE	254	1905
3	WING	151	1130
4	WING	90	675
5	WING (COLLECTOR)	146	1095
6	WING	154	1153
7	WING	279	2093
8	WING	173	1295
9	EXTERNAL TANK (LONG RANGE)	500	3750

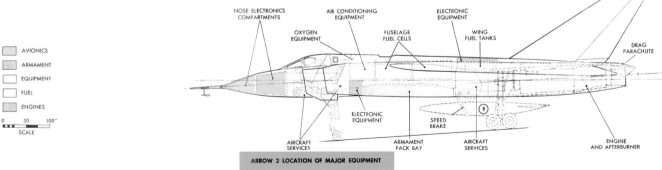

AVIONICS

ARMAMENT

EQUIPMENT

FUEL

ENGINES

0   50   100"
SCALE

ARROW 2 LOCATION OF MAJOR EQUIPMENT

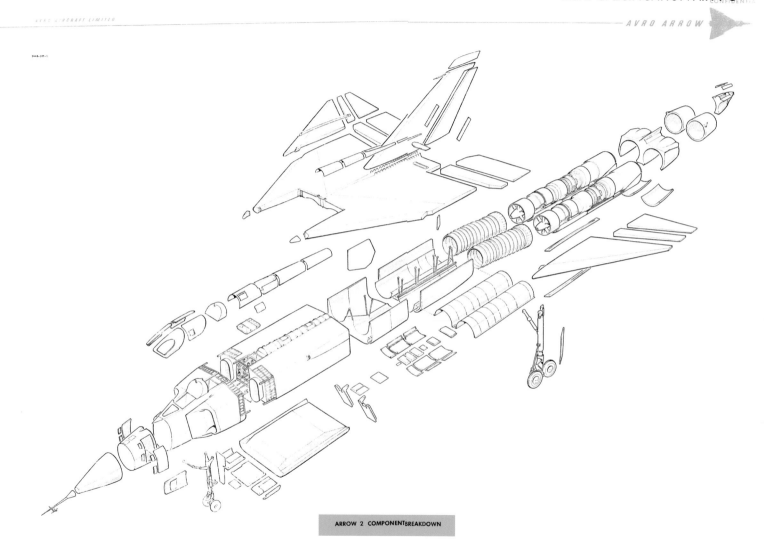

ARROW 2 COMPONENT BREAKDOWN

SUPERSONIC SENTINEL

PROVING THE DESIGN

Free flight Arrow model launch

Stability and control wind tunnel model

The CF-105 is to be build using the Cook-Craigie plan. This means that the first aircraft will be manufactured from production type tooling and drawings. To minimize the risks involved in choosing this method, design, structure, component and systems testing are required. One of the first steps is to gather aerodynamic and control data using wind tunnel scale models and free flight models.

Flutter wind tunnel scale model

Full size wooden mock-up

Full size metal mock-up

In order to help the design and engineering teams, CF-105 full scale wood and metal mock-ups are built. These three-dimensional mock-ups help the teams not only as tools proving devices, but also as development tools. They are also used for training production crews and for engineering reviews.

Flight simulator

Truck mounted cockpit mock-up

To help engineers in designing the cockpit, a mock-up of the front section is mounted on a truck and simulates the actual height and attitude of the aircraft. A flight simulator is set-up with visual representation of the CF-105 attitude, rate of climb, stability, engine noise inputs and more. A considerable amount of crew training will be performed on this device prior to the aircraft's first flight.

CF-105 Fatigue Test Article

CF-100 armed with four Sparrow II missiles

Extensive component structural and systems testing is performed using complete structural static test rigs to check the aircraft load limits. For armament, the Sparrow II missile which will be used by the CF-105 is tested on a modified CF-100 aircraft.

SUPERSONIC SENTINEL

MANUFACTURING AND ASSEMBLY

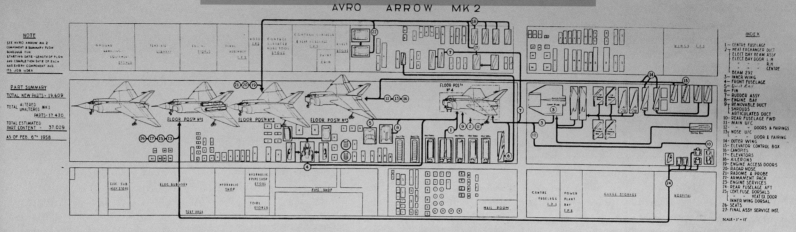

MASTER MANUFACTURING SEQUENCE
AVRO ARROW MK 2

Over 17,000 engineering drawings are released to the manufacturing division for production planning and tooling prior to the CF-105 rollout.

Nose section in jig

Engine bay enclosure jig

15,000 ton hydraulic rubber pad forming press

Vertical fin in jig

Fuselage centre section production line

The CF-105 program uses over 1,500,000 square feet (139,350 square meters) of floor space at Avro.

Inner wing being positioned to fuselage

Engine bay enclosure positioned for installation to main delta platfo

Arrow final assembly line

650 suppliers are contracted for the aircraft program, creating work for 5,000 specialized workers outside Avro in the manufacture of CF-105 part and tools

SUPERSONIC SENTINEL

ORENDA PS-13 IROQUOIS

The supersonic turbojet
previously designated the PS-13—
for Project Study 13—
now reaching maturity,
is christened

IROQUOIS

ORENDA
ENGINES LIMITED
MALTON, CANADA
MEMBER: A. V. ROE CANADA LIMITED & THE HAWKER SIDDELEY GROUP

Charles A. Grinyer

Earle K. Brownridge

Based on the success of its series of turbojet engines powering the Avro CF-100 and Canadair F-86 Sabre, Orenda starts the design of a new engine known as PS-13 in September of 1953. The design team and staff are led by Charles A. Grinyer, Vice-President Engineering and Earle K. Brownridge, Executive Vice-President and General Manager.

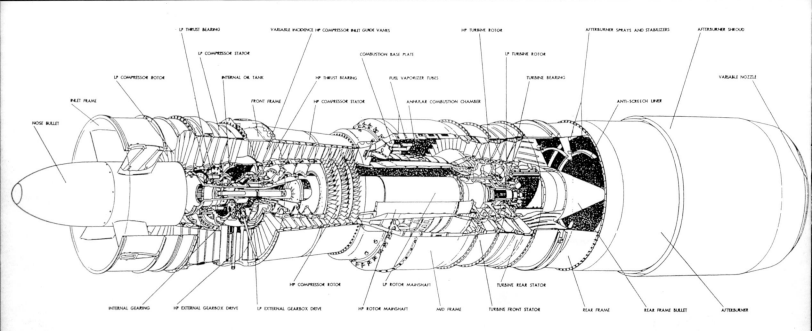

LP THRUST BEARING · VARIABLE INCIDENCE HP COMPRESSOR INLET GUIDE VANES · HP TURBINE ROTOR · AFTERBURNER SPRAYS AND STABILIZERS · AFTERBURNER SHROUD

LP COMPRESSOR STATOR · COMBUSTION BASE PLATE · LP TURBINE ROTOR

LP COMPRESSOR ROTOR · INTERNAL OIL TANK · HP THRUST BEARING · FUEL VAPORIZER TUBES · TURBINE BEARING · VARIABLE NOZZLE

INLET FRAME · FRONT FRAME · HP COMPRESSOR STATOR · ANNULAR COMBUSTION CHAMBER · ANTI-SCREECH LINER

NOSE BULLET

INTERNAL GEARING · HP EXTERNAL GEARBOX DRIVE · LP EXTERNAL GEARBOX DRIVE · HP COMPRESSOR ROTOR · LP ROTOR MAINSHAFT · TURBINE REAR STATOR · REAR FRAME · REAR FRAME BULLET · AFTERBURNER

HP ROTOR MAINSHAFT · MID FRAME · TURBINE FRONT STATOR

AVRO IROQUOIS MK1
"Dominant Indian Tribe"
Design Started - September 14, 1953
Design Thrust - 19250 LB. (Dry)
- 26000 LB.(Wet)
First Run - December 15, 1954

The PS-13 is a twin-spool turbojet engine with an integral afterburner design to have a thrust-to-weight ratio of better than 5:1. It can produce a sea-level dry thrust of about 20,000 lbs (9,070 kg) and 26,000 lbs (11,795 kg) with afterburning.

PS-13 Iroquois assembly

PS-13 Iroquois Mk.2

CF-105 aircraft number 6 will be the first to be equipped with the new turbojet engine. On July 22nd 1957, the PS-13 is officially christened "Iroquois." A few days later, the engine passes the official 100 hour endurance test which equals to 400 hours of "military flying time."

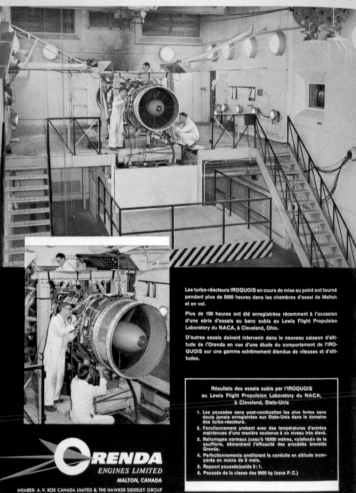

Répétition avant Mach 3 à 30 000 mètres

Les turbo-réacteurs IROQUOIS en cours de mise au point ont tourné pendant plus de 5000 heures dans les chambres d'essai de Malton et en vol.

Plus de 100 heures ont été enregistrées récemment à l'occasion d'une série d'essais au banc subis au Lewis Flight Propulsion Laboratory du NACA, à Cleveland, Ohio.

D'autres essais doivent intervenir dans le nouveau caisson d'altitude de l'Orenda en vue d'une étude du comportement de l'IROQUOIS sur une gamme extrêmement étendue de vitesses et d'altitudes.

Résultats des essais subis par l'IROQUOIS au Lewis Flight Propulsion Laboratory du NACA, à Cleveland, Etats-Unis

1. Les poussées sans post-combustion les plus fortes sans doute jamais enregistrées aux Etats-Unis dans le domaine des turbo-réacteurs.
2. Fonctionnement probant avec des températures d'entrées maintenues d'une manière soutenue à un niveau très élevé.
3. Rallumages normaux jusqu'à 18000 mètres, plafond de la soufflerie, démontrant l'efficacité des procédés brevetés Orenda.
4. Perfectionnements améliorant la conduite en altitude incorporés en moins de 2 mois.
5. Rapport poussée/poids 5:1.
6. Poussée de la classe des 9000 kg (sans P.C.).

ORENDA ENGINES LIMITED
MALTON, CANADA
MEMBER: A. V. ROE CANADA LIMITED & THE HAWKER SIDDELEY GROUP

Rehearsal for Mach 3 at 100,000 feet

IROQUOIS development engines have completed over 5,000 hours of bench running in these test cells at Malton and in flight tests.

Over 100 hours were accumulated during a recent series of test runs at the NACA Lewis Flight Propulsion laboratory, Cleveland, Ohio.

Further tests will be conducted in Orenda's new high altitude facility to investigate IROQUOIS performance over the widest range of speed and altitude.

IROQUOIS test results at NACA Lewis Flight Propulsion laboratory, Cleveland, U.S.A.

1. Probably highest dry thrusts recorded in North America for turbojets.
2. Successful operation under sustained high inlet temperatures.
3. Normal relights up to 60,000 feet, the limit of the tunnel, proved effectiveness of Orenda patented method.
4. Altitude handling improvements incorporated within two months.
5. Thrust/weight 5:1.
6. Thrust—in the 20,000 lb. class (without afterburner).

ORENDA ENGINES LIMITED
MALTON, CANADA
MEMBER: A. V. ROE CANADA LIMITED & THE HAWKER SIDDELEY GROUP

X 059

Boeing TB-47B / Canadair CL-52
Iroquois flying test bed

Flight testing of the Iroquois is necessary to gather the data needed for its certification. Orenda receives a Boeing TB-47B on loan from the USAF in order to accomplish this work. Canadair is subcontracted to modify the aircraft which is known as the CL-52. On November 12, 1957, the Orenda PS-13 Iroquois runs at altitude for the first time.

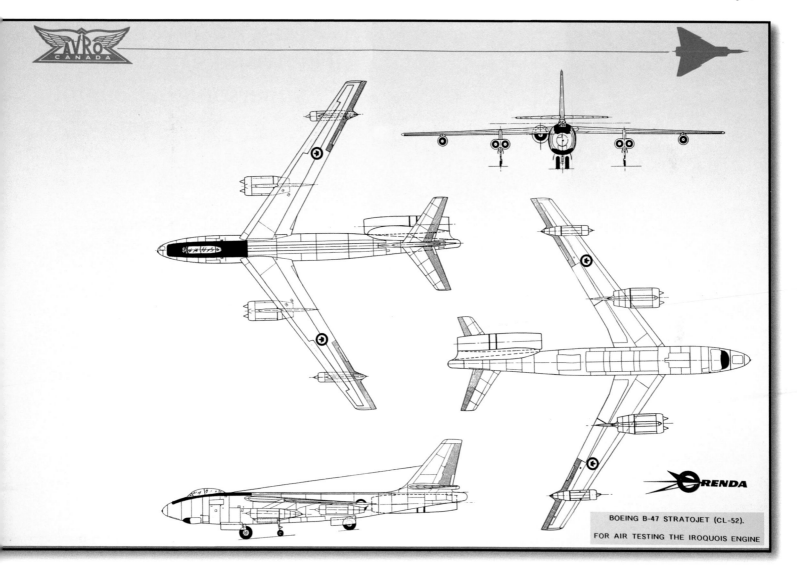

BOEING B-47 STRATOJET (CL-52).

FOR AIR TESTING THE IROQUOIS ENGINE

The CL-52 / Iroquois flying test bed aircraft over Lake Ontario, November 1957.

SUPERSONIC SENTINEL

ROLLOUT - OCTOBER 4, 1957

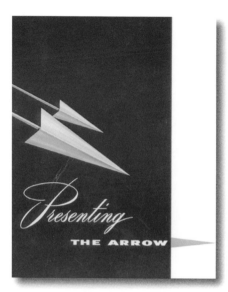

AVRO AIRCRAFT LIMITED

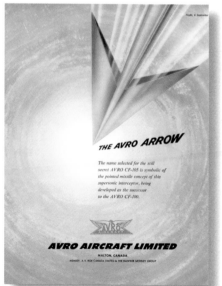

THE AVRO ARROW

The name selected for the still
secret AVRO CF-105 is symbolic of
the pointed missile concept of this
supersonic interceptor, being
developed as the successor
to the AVRO CF-100.

AVRO AIRCRAFT LIMITED
MALTON, CANADA
MEMBER, A. V. ROE CANADA LIMITED & THE HAWKER SIDDELEY GROUP

welcome

On behalf of all of us at Avro, may
I extend a cordial welcome to this
historic unveiling of Canada's first
supersonic aircraft, the CF-105, Avro
Arrow interceptor

program

Band of the Royal Canadian Air Force

God Save the Queen

Fred. T Smye,
President and General Manager,
Avro Aircraft Limited

Air Marshal H. L. Campbell, C.B.E., C.D.,
Chief of Air Staff,
Royal Canadian Air Force

Hon. George R. Pearkes, V.C.,
Minister of National Defence

MALTON ONTARIO OCTOBER 4, 1957

Rollout documents

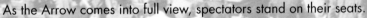

As the Arrow comes into full view, spectators stand on their seats.

Charlie Parker, 1957

Charlie Parker, 2011

The future, looking at the future!

More than 1,000 VIPs representing the militaries of Canada, the US, and other NATO countries, as well as from the aviation industry and the Canadian Government are in Malton to witness the unveiling of Canada's first supersonic aircraft, the Avro CF-105 Arrow.

Another 10,000 spectators including Avro employees, aviation writers and photographers are also present for this great moment. The first Arrow has been built in only twenty-eight months, from the release of the first drawing in June of 1955 to its rollout.

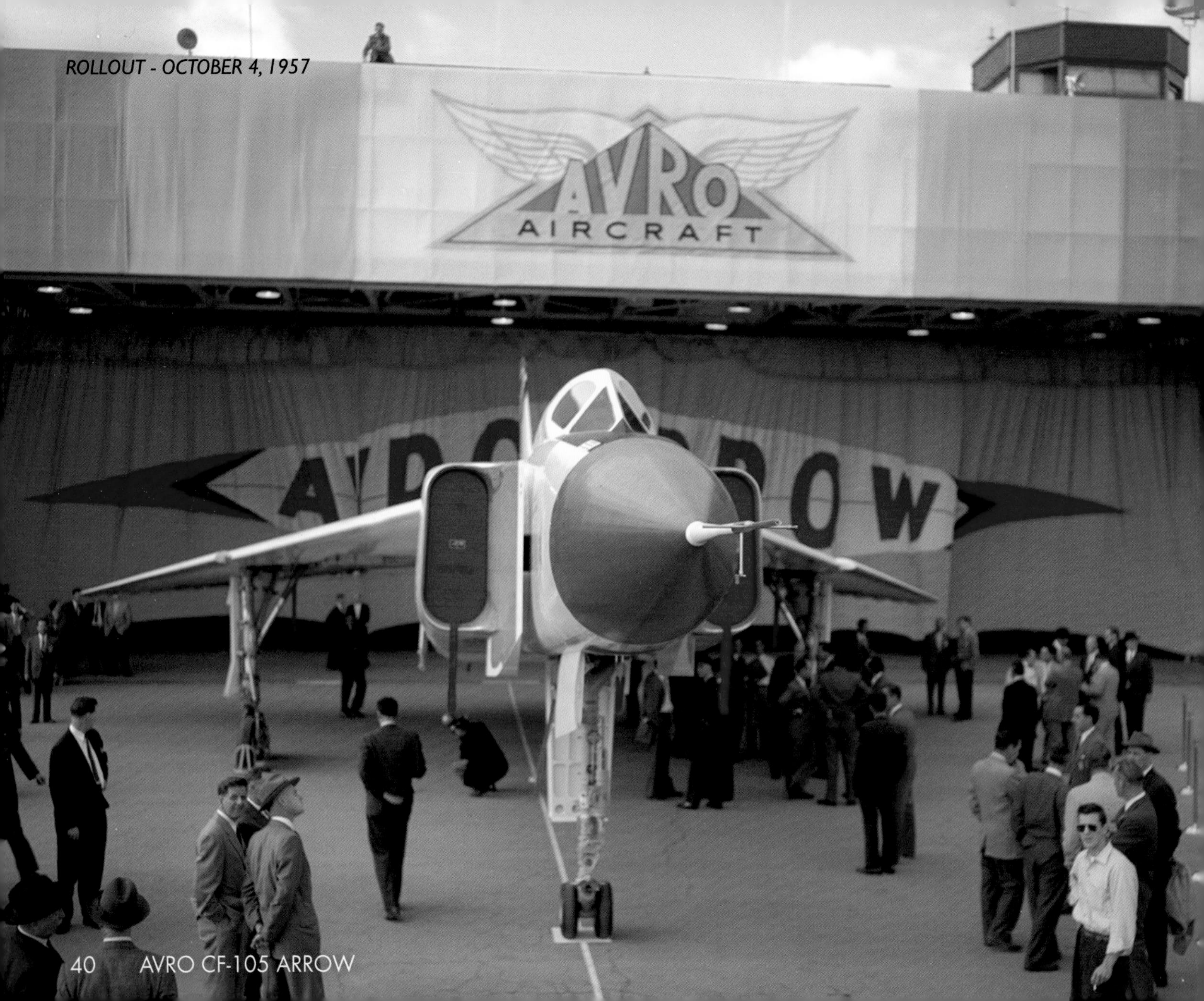

ROLLOUT - OCTOBER 4, 1957

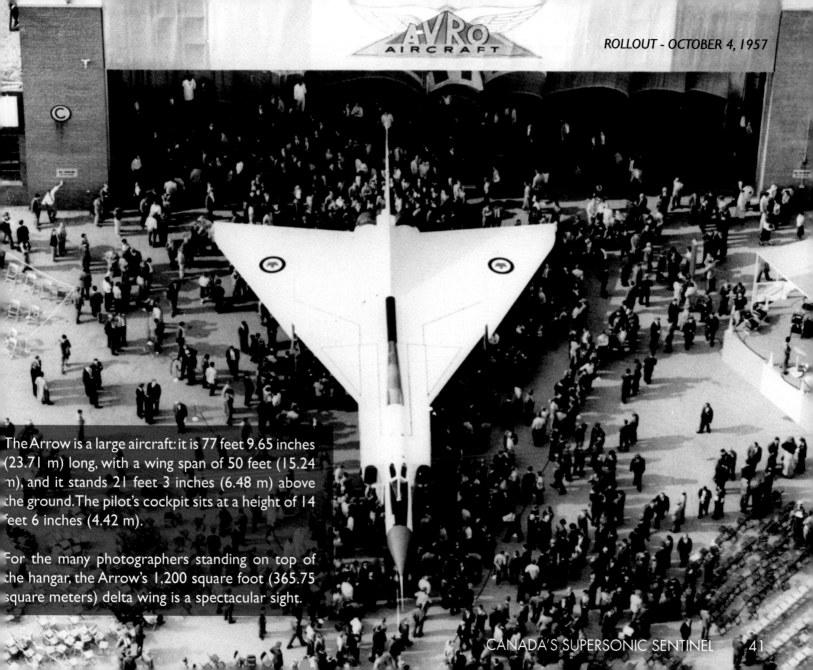

The Arrow is a large aircraft: it is 77 feet 9.65 inches (23.71 m) long, with a wing span of 50 feet (15.24 m), and it stands 21 feet 3 inches (6.48 m) above the ground. The pilot's cockpit sits at a height of 14 feet 6 inches (4.42 m).

For the many photographers standing on top of the hangar, the Arrow's 1,200 square foot (365.75 square meters) delta wing is a spectacular sight.

The Arrow pauses for official photograph.

The Arrow is towed away from rollout in direction of experimental hangar D2.

SUPERSONIC SENTINEL

GROUND TESTS AND TAXI TRIALS

P&W J75-P3 engine ground run

Winter taxi trial

First engine run occurs on December 4. As the Pratt & Whitney J75-P3 comes to life, the water injected into the jet stream to cool the muffler unit, causes large clouds of steam in this very cold temperature. Both engines are tested together for the first time on December 18. Six days later, the CF-105 runs on its own power.

Runway 14/32 (11,050 feet / 3,368 m) is used for the trials. It is the longest and widest runway at Malton airport. The trials are done in two phases, low and high speed. In mid-March, both pilot and aircraft are ready for the first flight.

Evening taxi trial

Jan Zurakowski climbs down from cockpit after another taxi trial.

SUPERSONIC SENTINEL

AN ARROW IN THE SKY

Tuesday March 25th 1958, the Arrow is ready for its first flight. The engines are fired up and the aircraft is taxied to the end of runway 32. At 9:51 am, the brakes are released. At 120 knots (138 mph - 222 km/h), the nose wheel lifts off. At

The Arrow climbs to 5,000 feet (1,524 m) without afterburners. After a few checks, Jan Zurakowski selects gear up and applies more power. At an indicated speed of 250 knots (288 mph - 463 km/h), the aircraft climbs this time to 11, 000 feet (3,353 m) where it's flying characteristics are investigated.

After having cautiously explored the flight envelope, it's time to get the aircraft back on the ground. Zurakowski circles the airport several times so that those who have created the Arrow can see it fly. Thousands of workers have been released from their duties for the occasion.

Circling over the Avro plant prior to landing

Jubilant *Avroites* lift Chief Experimental test Pilot Jan Zurakowski off ground after successful first flight of the Arrow.

At 10:05 am, contact is made with the runway. The maiden flight of the Arrow has lasted thirty-five minutes.

SUPERSONIC SENTINEL

CF-105 FLIGHT TESTS

Arrow Test Pilots (l-r):
Avro's Spud Potocki and Peter Cope
RCAF F/Lt. Jack Woodman
Avro's Chief Test Pilot Jan Zurakowski

The first phase of the flight test program starts with the second flight on April 1st. The purpose of this phase is to extend the pilot's preliminary assessment of the handling qualities of the aircraft.

Two days later, on its third flight, the Arrow goes supersonic for the first time. At 15,000 feet (4,572 m), Zurakowski lights up the afterburners. The aircraft easily reaches 40,000 feet (12,192 m) and passes through the sound barrier. A speed of Mach 1.1 (720 mph - 1,160 km/h) is recorded.

On Friday April 18, a high speed run is carried out at 49,000 feet (14,935 m). The Arrow attains a speed of 1,000 mph (1,610 km/h - Mach 1.52). It also reaches a maximum altitude of 50,000 feet (15,240 m) during this flight. For the first time, the RCAF releases a press communique announcing the performance achieved by the CF-105.

On Tuesday April 22nd, Flight Lieutenant Jack Woodman becomes the RCAF's first pilot to fly the Arrow. His familiarization flight last an hour and ten minutes and he reaches a speed of Mach 1.4 (925 mph - 1490 km/h). The day after Woodman's flight, Spud Potocki becomes Avro's second test pilot to fly RL-201. He achieves a speed of Mach 1.2 (790 mph - 1,270 km/h) during this flight.

On June 11, Zurakowski brings the aircraft for landing after a normal flight. However, unknown to him, rotation of the left main landing gear is incomplete. The tandem wheels are at an angle to the landing path. On touchdown, the aircraft starts to veer off to the left and leaves the runway. Tires dig into the soft soil, deceleration is rapid and the landing gear collapses.

RL-201 is up flying again on October 5th.

At the end of July, the second Arrow has started its engine runs and taxi trials.

On August 1ˢᵗ, RL-202 becomes airborne for the first time. Over the next few weeks, it flies six times for a total of 6 hours and 35 minutes of flight time. Each flight achieves supersonic speeds up to Mach 1.72 (1,124 mph - 1,809 km/h).

Photo: Nick Wolochatiuk

On November 11th, Spud Potocki flies Arrow RL-202 to an altitude of 50,000 feet (15,240 m) and to a speed of Mach 1.96 (1,290 mph - 2,075 km/h). Upon landing, the main gear wheels lock. The tires explode and directional control is lost. The Arrow skids off the runway, the right main gear collapses and the aircraft comes to a halt with the right wingtip dragging on the ground.

On September 22nd, Arrow number three takes to the air. On its very first flight, the aircraft, piloted by Zurakowski exceeds the speed of sound achieving Mach 1.2 (785 mph - 1,265 km/h)

In early January 1959, the fifth Arrow starts its pre-flight testing. After a few days of checks and maintenance work,

SUPERSONIC SENTINEL

UNCERTAIN FUTURE

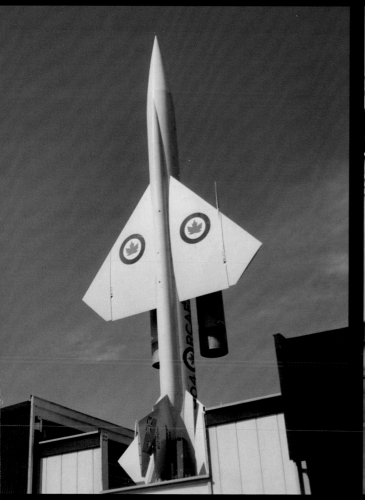

In September 1958, the Canadian Government orders the Boeing Bomarc missile. It can theoretically destroy enemy bombers before they can drop their payloads on military targets and industrial regions. However, it is not effective against intercontinental ballistic missiles.

446 Squadron, North Bay, ON

Unfortunately, this adds an additional expense to the already large Canadian defence budget. Furthermore, the Government uses the lower cost of the Bomarc against the high cost of the Arrow as a reason for selecting the missile.

447 Squadron, La Macaza, QC

Two RCAF squadrons will be equipped with the Bomarc starting in 1961. 446 Squadron is to be stationed at North Bay, Ontario, while 447 Squadron is to be stationed at La Macaza, Quebec. Each squadron will be armed with 28 Bomarc, including nuclear W40 warheads installed in the missiles at all times.

WITH THE INTRODUCTION OF THE BOMARC MISSILE, THE ARROW'S FUTURE IS CAST IN DOUBT.

SUPERSONIC SENTINEL

AVRO'S PROJECT RESEARCH GROUP

Painting: Randall L. Whitcomb

One of the objectives of Avro's Project Research Group is to do design studies on high-performance Arrow derivatives that would follow the Mk.2 version.

Arrow Mk.2A: increased high speed mission radius of 575 miles (925 km) and a low speed mission radius of 790 miles

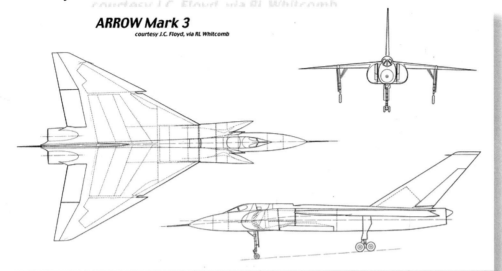

ARROW Mark 3
courtesy J.C. Floyd, via RL Whitcomb

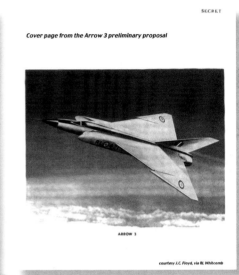

SECRET

Cover page from the Arrow 3 preliminary proposal

ARROW 3

courtesy J.C. Floyd, via RL Whitcomb

Painting: Randall L. Whitcomb

Arrow Mk.3: combat speed of Mach 3.0 (1,980 mph - 3,186 km/h) at 70,000 feet (31,752 m) with a high speed mission radius of 362 miles (583 km) and a low speed mission radius of 421 miles (678 km).

If this version becomes operational, the RCAF will be the only air force in the world to fly a Mach 3.0 aircraft in combat missions.

Painting: Randall L. Whitcomb

Arrow Mk.4: Long range / Sub-orbital interception / Tactical bombing / Anti-ICBM missile platform aircraft able to achieve sustained speeds of Mach 2.5, a combat speed of Mach 3.0 and a combat ceiling of 80,000 feet (24,384 m).

SUPERSONIC SENTINEL

ARROW MK.2 RL-206

DANGER 550 VOLTS

By February 1959, the first Arrow Mk.2 RL-206 is in final assembly. The Mk.2 performances will be superior to the Mk.1 version because its operational weight is 10% (4,000 lb. - 1,815 kg) less. The use of the more powerful Iroquois engine will allow the Mk.2 to easily exceed its estimated maximum level speed of Mach 2 (1,320 mph - 2,125 km/h) at 50,000 feet (15,240 m).

ARROW MK.2 RL-206

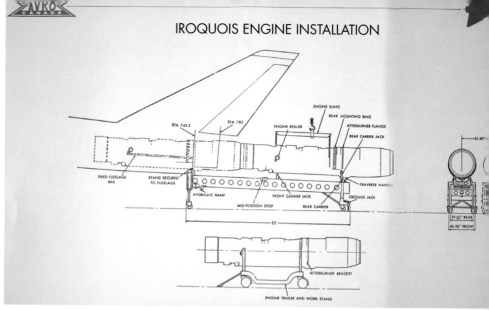

IROQUOIS ENGINE INSTALLATION

ENGINE SLING
REAR MOUNTING RING
AFTERBURNER FLANGE
REAR CARRIER JACK
TRAVERSE HANDLE
STA. 742.5
STA. 783
ENGINE ROLLER
FIXED FUSELAGE RAIL
STAND SECURED TO FUSELAGE
HYDRAULIC RAMP
MID-POSITION STOP
FRONT CARRIER JACK
REAR CARRIER
GROUND JACK
23'
61.40"
39.62" REAR
46.50" FRONT

AFTERBURNER BRACKET
ENGINE TRAILER AND WORK STAND

On February 5th, Iroquois engine S/N X-116 is the first of its type to be test-fitted in an Arrow.

RL-206 Pilot cockpit
Photo: Marc-André Valiquette

Department of National Defence

Royal Canadian Air Force

Malton Ont
20 Feb 59

Ref your Memo S1038CN-180 (AAWS) 03 Feb 59
from W/C Goss to G/C Foottit

9054 A

Referred to AAWS
FEB 23 1959
File 1037CN-180
Chg'd to AWSS 17/2/59

Chief of the Air Staff
Air Force Headquarters
Ottawa Ont

Attention AWS

Arrow Weapon System - Status of Aircraft 25206

1   As discussed with Mr. Wilf Taylor, the following report
outlines the status of Arrow 2 No 25206 as on 20 Feb 59.

(a) Airframe

   (i) Structure - complete.

   (ii) Engine Bay - assumed complete until verified
        by engine installation.

   (iii) Cockpit - complete except for the throttle
         box which is undergoing some rework.

   (iv) Flying Control - hydraulic installation pro-
        gressing favourably, still a few pipes short.
        Damping system installed and functioning tests
        well advanced.

   (v) Fuel System - Minor changes to fuel sequenc-
        ing being carried out.

   (vi) Electrical System - installation and contin-
        uity tests complete. Functioning tests of
        the equipment 50% complete. Alternator and
        CSU being run on rig.

   (vii) Shortages - Water boiler now installed (no
         longer a shortage.

         Telecom - all equipment now at Avro 90%
                   installed.

(b) Engines

   (i) Engine 107 - suffered a blade failure on
        initial run and is being set up again for
        final 50 hour PFRT.

   (ii) Engine 115 - has been modified and has com-
        pleted its bench check and green strip.
        Upon strip a failed ball was found in the
        thrust bearing, but this is considered an
        isolated case. It still is planned that
        this engine will be delivered to Avro by
        the 28 Feb and will be considered flight
        worthy.

   (iii) Engine 116 - the status of this engine is
         undecided at present due to the implications
         of the blade failure on engine 107.

                                        Contd ......

- 2 -

   (iv) Engine 117 - no change.

(c) Engine runs originally scheduled to commence on
    the 20 February are not likely to commence until
    the 06 March. Problems arising from engine run-
    ning will then become even more critical, and
    although Avro are still aiming at first flight
    by the end of March, it appears very unlikely
    that this can be met. Your estimate of end of
    April or 1st of May is considered realistic by
    the TSD.

                        (HS Crosby) S/L
                for Acting Detachment Commander 1202 TSD
                        Avro Aircraft Ltd

On February 20th, a status report is provided to the Chief of the Air Staff Hugh Campbell about Arrow RL-206. It states that engine runs are not likely to begin before March 6 and that a first flight by May 1st is considered realistic.

SUPERSONIC SENTINEL

BLACK FRIDAY

On Friday morning February 20, 1959, Canadian Prime Minister John Diefenbaker announces in the House of Commons that the Arrow and Iroquois are cancelled.

As a nation which owes much to aviation for its economic development and its place today in world councils, Canada is this year paying a special tribute to the nation's pioneers and achievements in aviation in observance of the Golden Anniversary of Flight in Canada.

THE SUPERSONIC AVRO ARROW

AVRO AIRCRAFT LIMITED

"All work is to be stopped forthwith and no further costs are to be incurred. No other work will be made available to the companies."

At 4:00 p.m, 9,500 employees at Avro and another 4,500 at Orenda are out of a job.

First 50 years of powered flight in Canada

1909-1959

From the DART in 1909 to the Arrow in 1959 a pattern of aeronautical accomplishment has been dramatically recorded in Canada. The past half century of Canada's growth and increasing stature has been greatly accelerated by the swift and vigorous momentum of the men and machines of the Air Age.

Well established in the Jet Age, Canada's aeronautical resources will continue to meet the urgent requirements of a nation on wings.

AVRO AIRCRAFT LIMITED

MEMBER: A. V. ROE CANADA LIMITED & THE HAWKER SIDDELEY GROUP

MARCH, 1959
VOL. 5, NO. 4

Avro
NEWSMAGAZINE

Special Supplement

Arrow Program Terminated
Company To Carry On, President Reports

The following message is directed by Mr. J. L. Plant, President and General Manager, to Avro personnel:

AT this writing, a total of some 1600 personnel are back at work at Avro on contracts remaining after the Government's cancellation of the Arrow program.

Weekly and hourly paid personnel who have returned to work were recalled on the basis of their seniority in occupational groups and in accordance with the terms of the Collective Agreements with the Company's Unions.

They form the nucleus of the company we are endeavouring to reorganize on the foundation of the Avro we have known over the past years.

It is gratifying to note the dispatch with which the re-hiring of personnel was made possible by the dedicated Avroites who virtually worked the clock around in order to give every possible attention to their task. It is also encouraging to note the complete co-operation in this matter from the National Employment Service. Without this concentration of effort by all concerned we would still be engaged in the great mass of detail that is obviously associated with the termination of employment of some 9,000 people, and an effort to re-employ as many as possible in the shortest possible time.

The Government order to terminate all work on the Arrow program came to us suddenly. A rumor started around the factory that the Arrow program had been terminated. Later, we learned that this rumor emanated from radio bulletins.

On confirming the truth and fact of these radio reports from the representative at Avro of the Department of Defence Production, Mr. C. A. Hore, it became imperative that I advise the company's personnel of this announcement.

When I sat down in front of the company's Public Address system microphone in the little brick building opposite Gate 9 to announce the Arrow cancellation, it was one of the toughest jobs I've ever undertaken. How do you tell some 9,000 people that the job they have been dedicated to, for years, has been cancelled? How do you tell them that the product of their minds and hands has been eliminated?

These were my remarks:

'The radio has recently announced the Prime Minister has stated in the House of Commons this morning that the Avro Arrow and Iroquois programs have been terminated.

'We, the Management of the company had no official information prior to this announcement being made. The cancellation of the Arrow and the Iroquois has, however, been confirmed as a fact by Mr. C. A. Hore, the representative here of the Department of Defence Production.

'It is impossible at this stage to give you any further details until such time as I receive the official telegram from Ottawa. In the meantime I would ask that you continue with your work. Later on in the day you will be informed as to our future. Thank you.'

As the morning of the contract termination progressed into early afternoon, it became apparent that the first step to be taken was to give notice of termination to all workers, and *(Continued on Page 2)*

SUPERSONIC SENTINEL

DESTRUCTION OF A DREAM

Following *Black Friday*, the five completed Arrow Mk.1 are moved inside the flight test hangar. In the assembly bay, 32 Arrow Mk 2 at various stages of completion await their fate.

RL-206

RL-207

RL-208

In early April, Defence Minister George Pearkes agrees to Air Marshall Hugh Campbell proposal's that all the assembled airframes be reduced to scrap. No Arrow is to be preserved for posterity.

Photo : Russell Fednews

RL-203
RL-204
RL-201
RL-205
RL-202

By mid-April, the five flyable Arrow Mk.1 have been moved out of the flight test hangar. July 10 has been set as a target date for complete dismantling of these aircraft. Inside the production hangar, destruction of all tooling, spares and Mk.2 Arrow airframes has started.

By July 6, three of the five Arrow Mk. I have been reduced to scrap. The fourth and the fifth aircraft are dismantled by July 10 and 17 respectively.

Photo: Herb Nott

On July 22nd, the five Arrow Mk. I aircraft are officially struck off charge from the RCAF.

SUPERSONIC SENTINEL

THE ARROW LIVES ON

Although the government has ordered that everything related to the Arrow be destroyed, a few items have survived. Large artefacts can be seen today at Canada's Aviation and Space museum in Rockcliffe, ON, thanks to the effort and determination of the museum's first interim Curator in 1960, M.S. "Mac" Kuhring.

Photos: Marc-André Valiquette

RL-203 Outer wing panels

RL-206 Cockpit

EMERGENCY
CANOPY OPENING

PS-13 Iroquois turbojet engine

Bristol, England, January 1961

S&S Turbine, March 2011

Robin Sipe, S&S Turbine, March 2014

In 1960, Iroquois engine serial X-116 is loaned to Bristol Siddeley Engines of England. After having been studied and tested, the turbojet is dismantled, stored and forgotten. In 2011, President of S&S Turbine Services Ltd. Robin Sipe brings the engine back to Canada. The plan is to test run X-116 once assembly is completed at their Fort St. John, BC test cell facility. They do not wish to test the engine to its limits, but merely want to hear an Iroquois engine run once again on Canadian soil. When the test runs are completed, the engine is to be donated to a Canadian aviation museum.

CASM Arrow Replica, 2006
Photo: Marc-André Valiquette

Over the years, many reunions, events, documentaries and a television miniseries help keep the Arrow memory alive. In 2006, the Canadian Air and Space Museum Arrow full-scale replica unveiling is the culminating event for the *Arrowheads* community. In September 2013, it was moved by road from Downsview Park to the International Centre in Mississauga (adjacent to Lester B. Pearson Airport) for public viewing at the SME Canadian Manufacturing Technology Show. This was a symbolic journey of the replica back to Malton where the original CF-105 Arrow was developed and built.

SUPERSONIC SENTINEL

EPILOGUE

On February 20, 1959, John Diefenbaker's Government announced its decision to cancel the Avro Arrow program. This resulted not only in the loss of a promising aircraft and turbojet engine; it was also the virtual disintegration of Canada's aviation industry in the aftermath of what became known as *Black Friday*.

It is my view that this was, for many reasons, the wrong decision. Nothing since 1976, when I started my research on the subject, has changed my belief that this decision was a political/economic one and had absolutely no basis in continental air defence requirements as military authorities saw them. And for all the reasons given for the cancellation, not one has stood the test of time.

First, cancelling the project using cost as an excuse was distorted. The money spent ($347,669,537 including termination costs) should have been seen as a production investment which could only be justified or assessed on the basis of predicted future production. It should not have been applied against the small number of test aircraft on contract at the time (37), which all critics have used then and since. Furthermore, The Financial Post September 20, 1958 front-page article titled *Your business and the Arrow's fate* had estimated that the government was recovering close to 65 per

Second, the ensuing layoffs dealt a severe blow to the Canadian aviation industry, which at that time was highly dependent on both Avro and Orenda. These companies had made a point of establishing Canadian sources of supply for their projects. Consequently, local firms had been introduced to many new techniques and processes, while large and talented design teams had been built up. Following the program cancellation, the contributions they made to Canada's prestige and capabilities virtually disappeared. The annihilation of Avro based on circumstances created largely by the government clearly ran against the long-term industrial interests of Canada.

Third, termination not only meant that the CF-105 full potential could not be demonstrated (32 Arrow Mk.2s were on the assembly line), it also curtailed the Iroquois' final weeks of testing. The turbojet sale to Dassault of France to equip the Mirage 4 bomber (300 engines) was consequently not concluded. This alone would have generated 120 million dollars in export sales and saved the Arrow project 40 million dollars. By continuing the CF-105, the flight test portion would have been completed and some aircraft would have been used operationally by the RCAF. Information gathered from the flight testing and operational service would have been invaluable when used in sales

Fourth, acquiring the Bomarc missile for the RCAF was not the answer to all of Canada's defence problems. American high-level government representatives sold the Canadian government and some high-ranking RCAF officers on the idea that the advent of missiles meant the obsolescence of all combat aircraft. Although cheaper than the Arrow and funded almost entirely by the U.S. ($91 million out of a total of $110.8 million), the Bomarc would prove to be useless against manned bombers only a few months after being acquired. And to be effective, the missile had to be armed with nuclear warheads which Diefenbaker refused to use. In hindsight, the government's conclusion that manned aircraft were becoming obsolete was obviously inaccurate, short-sighted, and absolutely wrong in every respect.

In the end, a great deal of the Canadian air force thinking had been predicated on the assumption that their budget was going to be restricted and therefore they could not acquire the Arrow and other military equipment. This unnecessary restriction dominated a lot of their deliberations and influenced their recommendations unfairly, since the budget envelope was not for the air force to determine. They should have stated their requirements to meet the military challenge, and leave the politicians to decide how much money would be budgeted in response. It is only by clearly defining requirements to meet anticipated defence threats that adequate funds will be secured to address them. If the initial assumption is that funding is inadequate, there can only be continuous retreat as the politicians dictate compromise and always scale back.

In 1959, Canada failed to appreciate the tremendous lead it was enjoying in military aerospace technology when it can

celled the Arrow. With Avro's demise, the country forever lost that lead, together with the export dollars it could have earned.

It was the wrong decision.

March 25, 2014 - 56th anniversary of the Arrow's first flight

Marc-Andre Valiquette
Author and Publisher
IMAVIATION